A record book for

_____

and

_____

"MEMORABLE
FIRSTS"

"THE STARS"

Her career	His career
_____	_____
_____	_____
_____	_____
_____	_____

Her hobbies and interests	His hobbies and interests
_____	_____
_____	_____
_____	_____
_____	_____

How she relaxes	How he relaxes
_____	_____
_____	_____
_____	_____
_____	_____

"THE BEGINNING"

How we met
_____
_____
_____
_____

Where we met
_____
_____

What attracted us to each other
_____
_____
_____

First impressions
_____
_____
_____

How long before we went out
_____
_____
_____

"THE FIRST DATE"

When

Where we went

Who asked whom

Best part of our date

We were most nervous about

Who called whom first

"FEATURE
PHOTOS"

"FEATURE
PHOTOS"

"OUR FIRST KISS"

When

Where

Who kissed whom

We'll always remember

"FEATURE
PHOTOS"

"OUR MOST EXCITING DATE"

When

_____

_____

Where we went

_____

_____

_____

What made it so exciting

_____

_____

_____

_____

_____

_____

_____

_____

"OUR MOST MISERABLE DATE"

When

_____

_____

Where we went

_____

_____

_____

Why it was so miserable

_____

_____

_____

_____

_____

_____

_____

_____

"I KNEW YOU LOVED ME WHEN..."

"SAYING THE 'L' WORD"

Who said it first
_____

When
_____
_____
_____

Where
_____
_____

His reaction
_____
_____
_____
_____
_____

Her reaction
_____
_____
_____
_____
_____

"FEATURE PHOTOS"

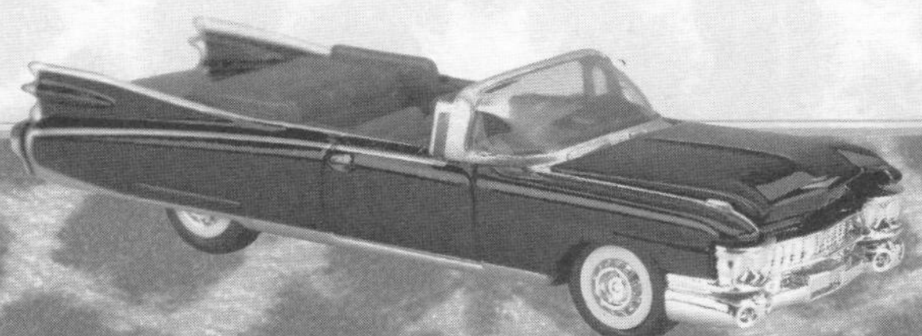

HIS _____

When _____

Where _____

What we did _____

How it went _____

"MEETING THE PARENTS"

HERS

_____

When _____

Where _____

_____

What we did _____

_____

_____

_____

How it went _____

_____

_____

_____

_____

_____

_____

_____

"MEMORABLE TRIPS"

Our First Trip

When

Where

What happened along the way

Our Favorite Trip

When

Where

What we did

"OUR MOST ROMANTIC GETAWAY"

When _____

Where _____

_____

Why it was so romantic _____

_____

_____

_____

_____

_____

_____

_____

_____

_____

_____

_____

_____

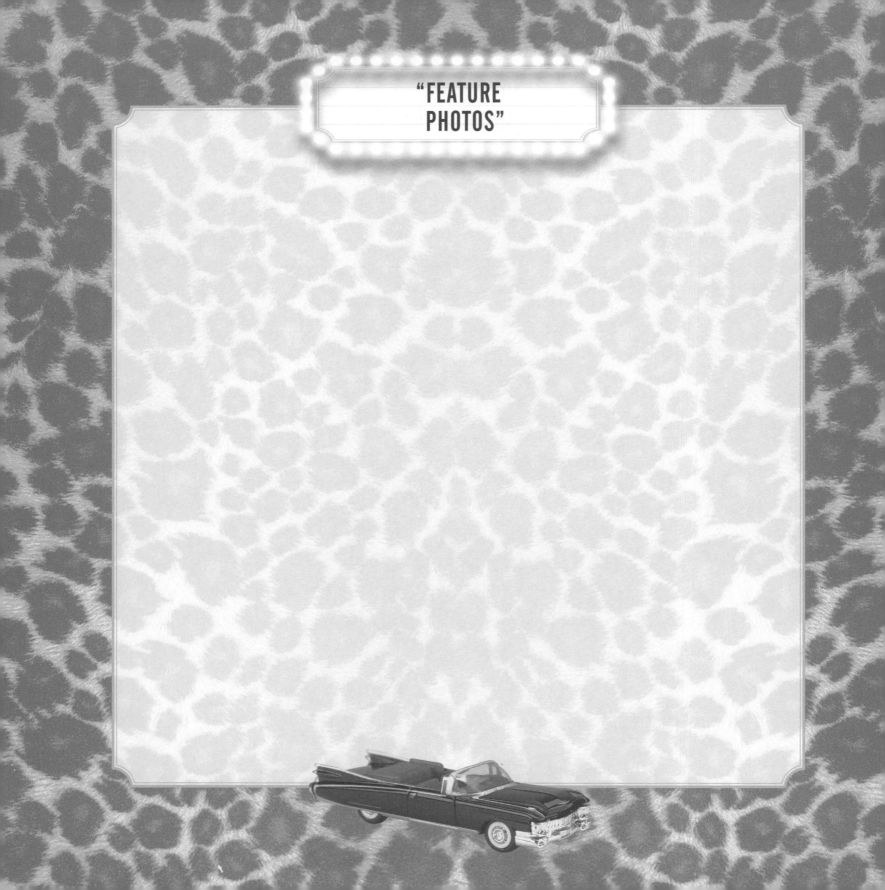

"FEATURE
PHOTOS"

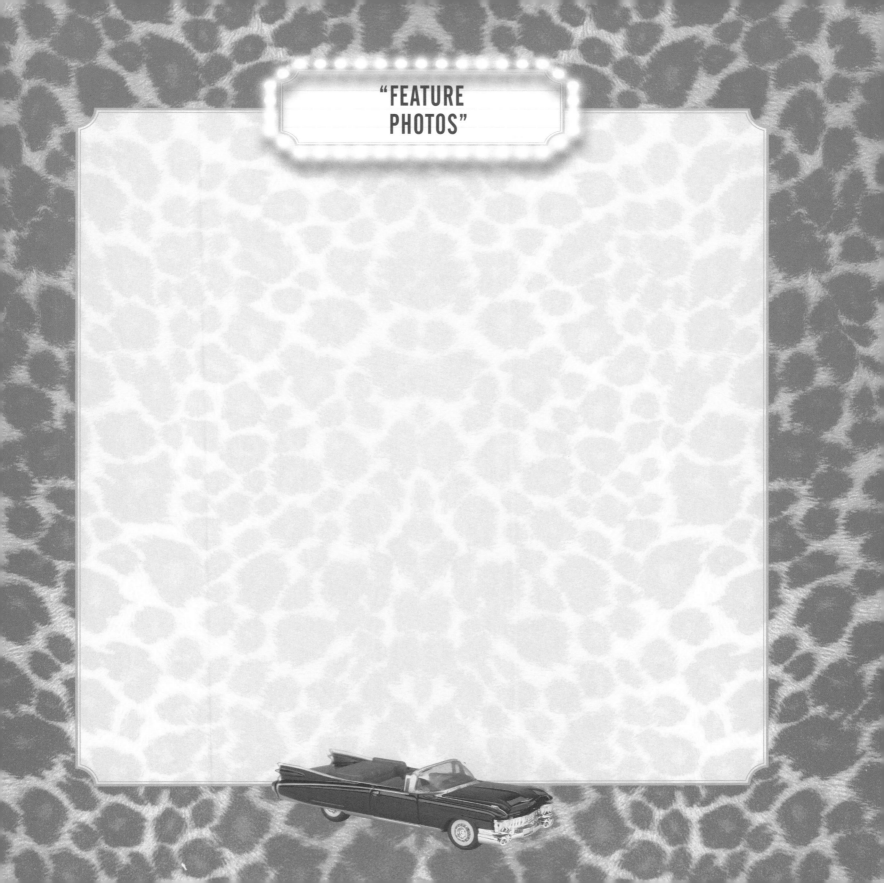

"FEATURE
PHOTOS"

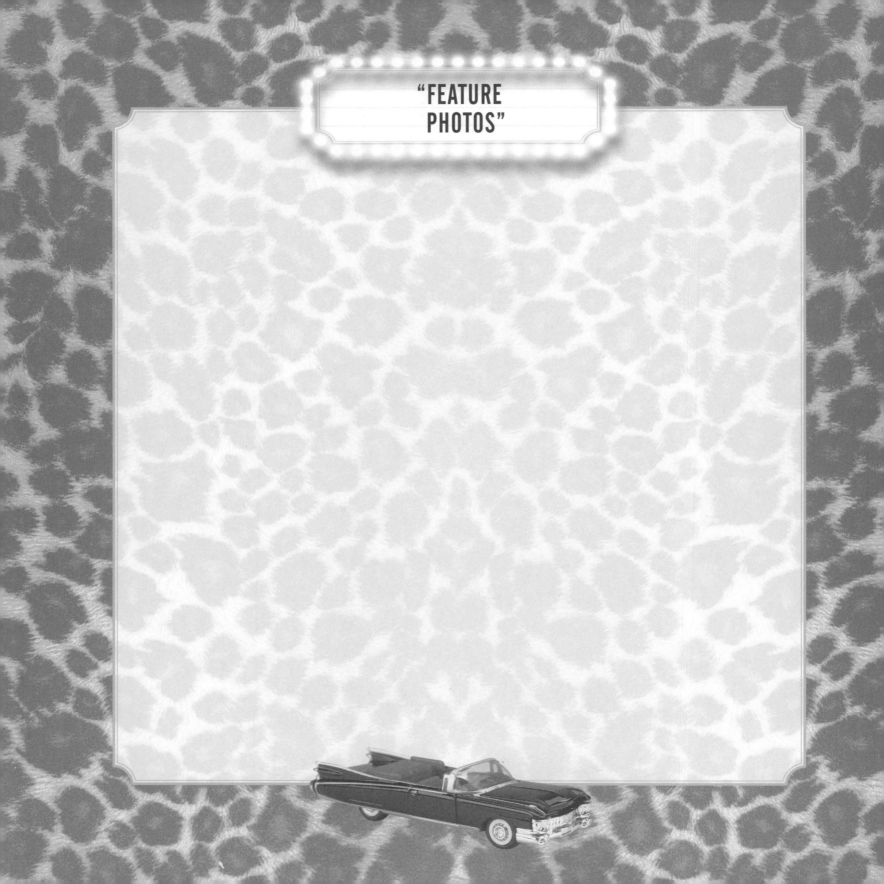

"FEATURE PHOTOS"

"TOKENS OF AFFECTION"

The first gift he gave her
_____

_____

His favorite gift _____

Why _____

_____

The most romantic gift _____

_____

The first gift she gave him _____

_____

Her favorite gift _____

Why _____

_____

The most romantic gift _____

_____

_____

_____

_____

_____

_____

"ALL ABOUT US"

"CELEBRATIONS"

His birthday _____

Her birthday _____

Anniversaries _____

_____

_____

_____

Holidays _____

_____

_____

Other special events _____

_____

How we spend them _____

_____

_____

_____

_____

_____

_____

"FEATURE PHOTOS"

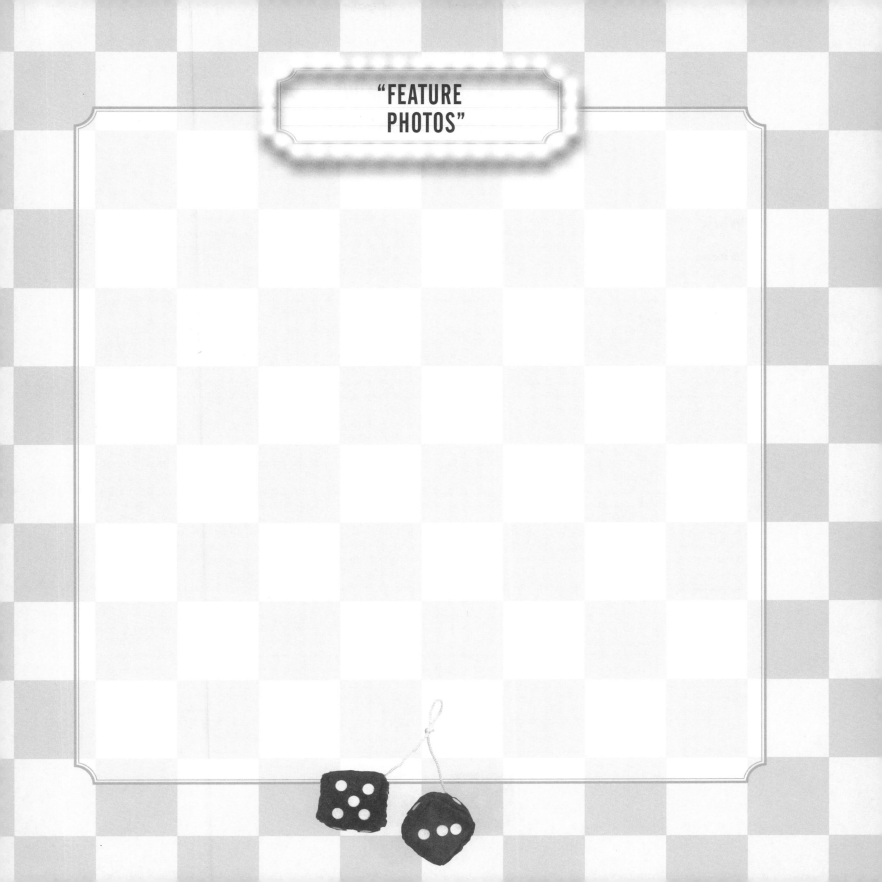

"FEATURE
PHOTOS"

"THE FIRST ITEM WE PURCHASED TOGETHER"

Item

When

Where

What it cost

Reason

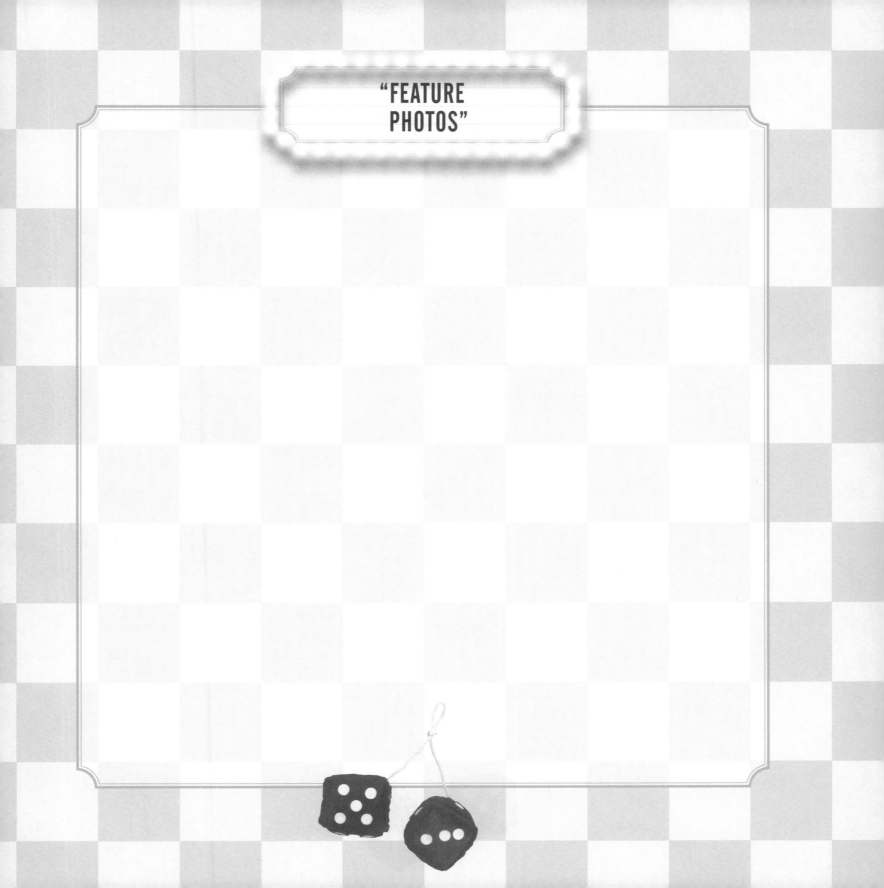

"FEATURE PHOTOS"

"OUR SIMILARITIES"

"OUR DIFFERENCES"

"BEST PHYSICAL ATTRIBUTES"

His
_____

_____

_____

_____

_____

Hers
_____

_____

_____

_____

_____

_____

_____

_____

"BEST PERSONALITY TRAITS"

What he loves most about her

_____
_____
_____
_____
_____
_____
_____

What she loves most about him

_____
_____
_____
_____
_____
_____
_____

"SENTIMENTAL
MEMORABILIA"

"SENTIMENTAL MEMORABILIA"

"FEATURE
PHOTOS"

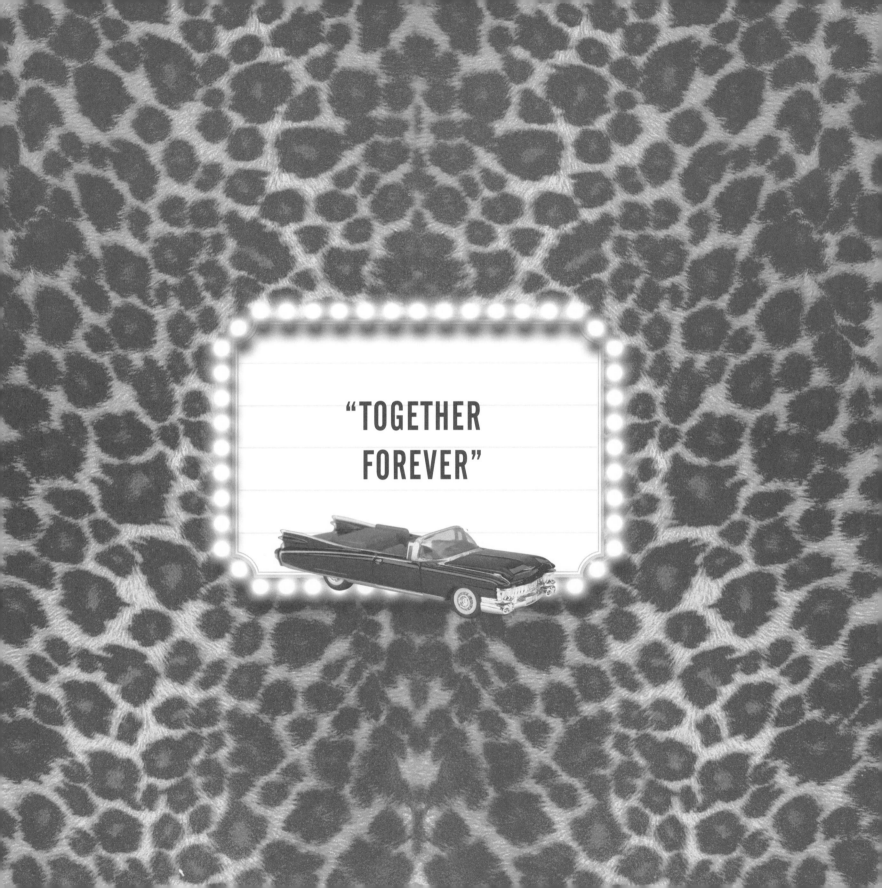

"TOGETHER FOREVER"

She sometimes calls him
_____
_____
_____
_____
_____
_____
_____
_____
_____

He sometimes calls her
_____
_____
_____
_____
_____
_____
_____
_____
_____

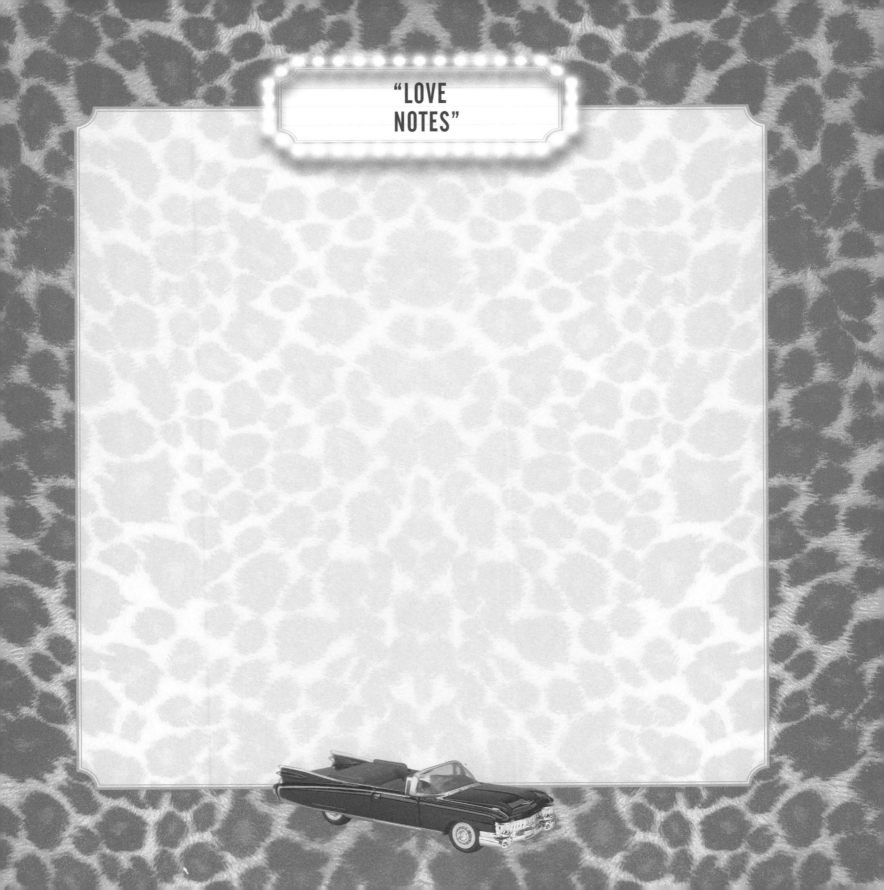

"LOVE NOTES"

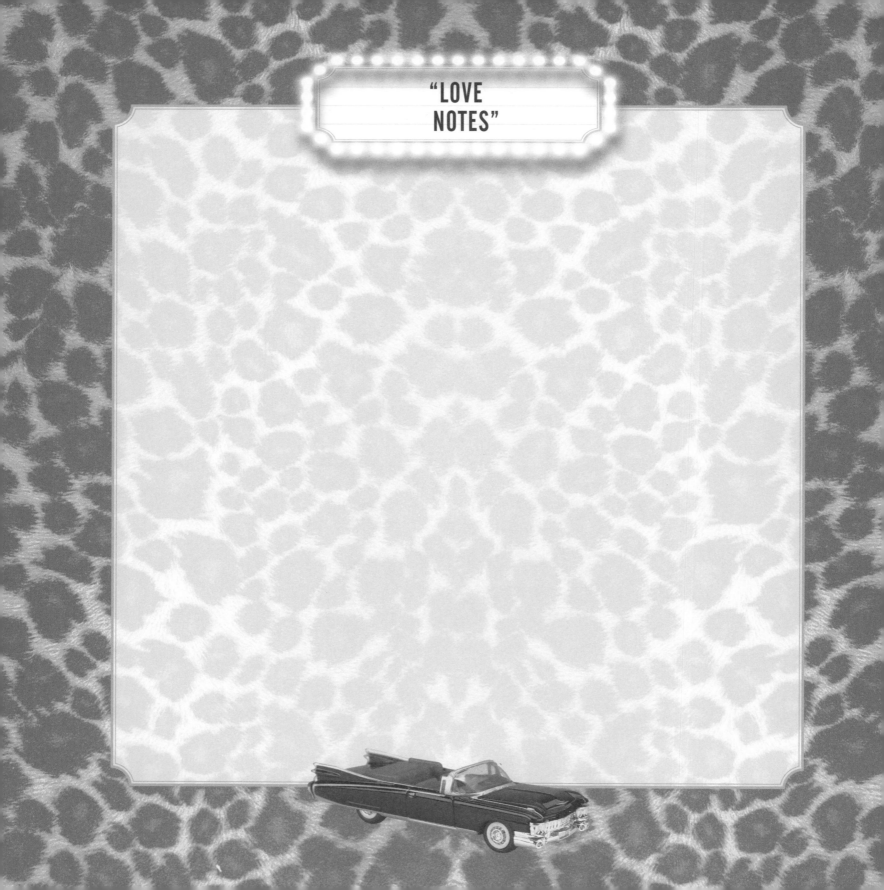

"LOVE
NOTES"

"THINGS WE SHOULD JUST DO ALONE"

His activities

_____

_____

_____

_____

_____

_____

Her activities

_____

_____

_____

_____

_____

_____

_____

"FAVORITE RAINY DAY ACTIVITIES"

Outdoors

_____

_____

_____

_____

_____

_____

_____

Indoors

_____

_____

_____

_____

_____

_____

_____

"THE BEST OF TIMES"

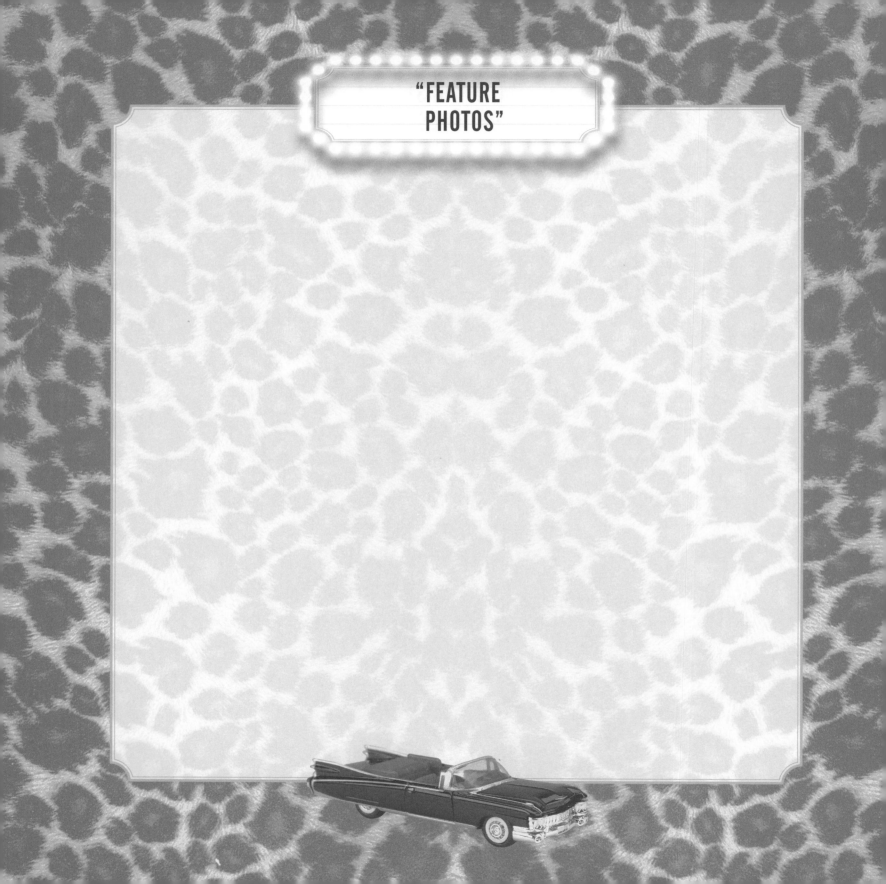

"FEATURE PHOTOS"

"FEATURE PHOTOS"

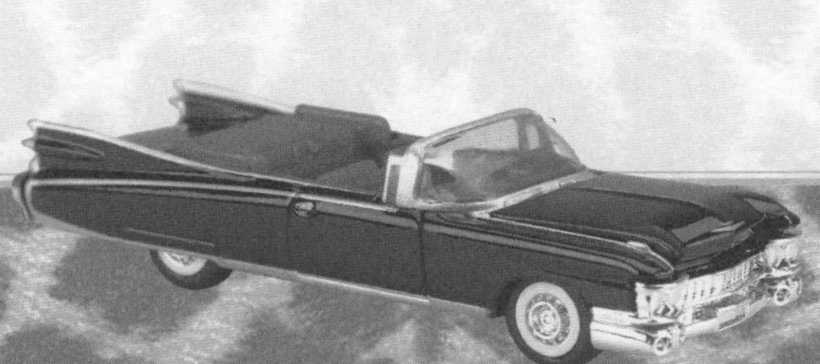

"TIME TOGETHER"

"FEAST ON THIS"

Favorite meal
_____
_____
_____

First meal he cooked for her
_____
_____
_____

First meal she cooked for him
_____
_____
_____

Favorite dessert
Foods he introduced to her
_____
_____
_____
_____

Foods she introduced to him
_____
_____
_____
_____

"FAVORITE
RECIPE"

"FAVORITE MENU"

"MUSICAL NOTES"

Our song

Why

Our first dance

When

Where

Song

His favorite group

Her favorite group

Music she introduced to him

Music he introduced to her

"FEATURE
PHOTOS"

"NIGHTS AT HOME"

Our favorite activities
_____
_____
_____
_____
_____

Our favorite meals
_____
_____
_____

Our favorite treats
_____
_____

Our favorite movie rentals
_____
_____
_____
_____
_____
_____
_____

"OUT ON THE TOWN"

Our favorite activities

_____

_____

_____

Our favorite restaurants

_____

_____

Our favorite dance clubs

_____

Our favorite theatres

_____

Our favorite plays/musicals

_____

New places he introduced to her

_____

_____

New places she introduced to him

_____

_____

_____

"PROGRAMS & TICKET STUBS"

"FEATURE
PHOTOS"

"FEATURE
PHOTOS"

"FEATURE
PHOTOS"

"FEATURE
PHOTOS"

"THE FUTURE"

What he wishes for

"THE FUTURE"

What she wishes for

"THE END"

© 2003 Havoc Publishing
San Diego, California
U.S.A.

ISBN 0-7416-1947-4

www.havocpub.com

Made in China

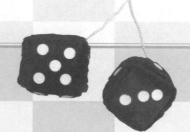

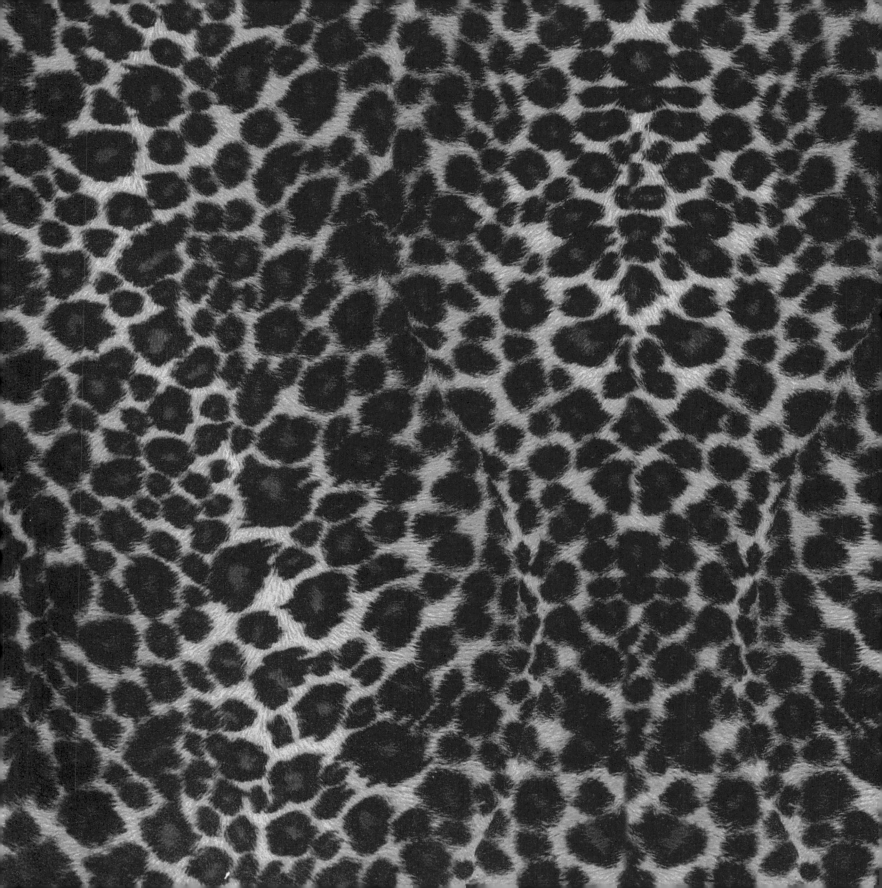